...ee ▶▶ to chocolate

Reception

Checking the beans

Roasting

Roasted beans

Mixing
separating the bean from the husk

Cocoa nibs

Crushing

Cocoa paste

Pressing

Pulverising the solid part (press cake)

Filtering the liquid part

Cocoa powder

Cocoa butter

INGREDIENTS

for WHITE CHOCOLATE: cocoa butter, sugar, milk, vanilla.

for MILK CHOCOLATE: cocoa butter and paste, sugar, milk, vanilla.

for DARK CHOCOLATE: cocoa butter and paste, sugar, vanilla.

Mixing the ingredients

Fine crushing

Conching
blending

Liquid chocolate

Tempering
reaching the right temperature

Coating

Moulding

Standard-size chocolates & over...

Bars, squares, Easter eggs, ...lded chocolates

Chocolatrium

GETTING TO KNOW WHAT CHOCOLATE IS ALL ABOUT

MICHEL CLUIZEL

A tribute to Marc & Marcelle Cluizel, my parents

Marc, Marcelle & Michel Cluizel.
(1973)

My parents, Marc and Marcelle Cluizel, were pastrychefs in Rambouillet, 45 kilometres south-west of Paris, for 14 years. They then settled in the small town of Damville, in Normandy, with the ambition of making high-quality chocolates for sale to the cake shops and confectioners of the area.

For their first year their kitchen doubled as their workshop. The year after, they set up a workshop in their back garden. The first three years of this small chocolate factory were difficult for the family. I decided nevertheless to follow my parents into the business and share their adventure in the world of chocolate.

Little by little, the reputation of Cluizel chocolates grew. One day, a confectionary salesman from the north of France convinced my father to give him some samples of his work. Just a few days later, the first orders arrived in the post, and in the months that followed there was a stream of confectionery salesmen knocking at the door.

With all the chocolates being made by hand, the growth in sales required more workers and larger premises. A new workshop was built on the family property,

quickly followed by another. In 1971, when an 1800 m² chocolate factory was built on the outskirts of the village, my parents and I were assisted by 40 workers.

As the years went by, the Cluizel business developed in many ways: more customers, more products, new premises, more staff, and modern, efficient equipment.

In 1984, my father passed away suddenly at the age of 77; my mother followed a few years later.

I thus found myself in the new role of head of the family and at the same time head of the business, acutely aware not only of my responsibilities towards the staff who already had every trust in me, but also of being alone in the task, with no one to fall back on for moral support.

Even now, when I walk through the silent workshops on a Sunday, I think back over the thirty-six years I spent working alongside my parents. Like them, I have always been convinced that machines could be used to make our products in the required quantities and to the required quality. The plant we have today convinces me a little more of this every day. Every workshop, every machine purchased before 1984 reminds me of the experiences we shared as a family, of the hard times, and the good times too.

When I think back to the family home where today's business started, I cannot but pay tribute to its founders, Marc Cluizel, father and master to his apprentice, and Marcelle, my mother and our guardian angel.

Michel Cluizel

Coating and rolling of the coated cores

The 1st spacious workshop

Cocoa and chocolate are two wonderful worlds of magic and passion.

I have been privileged to have had the extraordinary job of bringing them together: I find the best cocoa beans, grown by extraordinary people in distant lands, to make chocolates that tell a real story.

Through this album where photos, texts and cartoons mirror each other, I wish to share with you all, young and old, my experience of close to 60 years of enthralling work.

Very sincerely,

Michel Cluizel

Marc and Michel Cluizel visiting a plantation in the Dominican Republic, with the owner, Hector Rizek (November 2004).

"Developing direct relations with renowned planters, in a spirit of sustainable fair trade, is an opportunity to meet people of experience who live for and through their passions, and to guarantee the best possible traceability of cocoa."

Michel Cluizel

The legend of Quetzalcoatl

The story of cocoa began in Central America in the long-distant past. Perhaps more than 2,000 years ago. So long ago, in fact, that legend and history have become intermingled.

At that time, Europeans were unaware of the existence of the New World. They were unaware of the very existence of chocolate ... so could not suspect that within a few centuries they would be unable to do without it.

Central America was by no means unpopulated, however. It was home to some highly developed civilisations: the Mayas, the Toltecs, and later the Aztecs.

To them, everything was sacred: the quetzal - a bird with long, shimmering feathers -, snakes, maize. And a strange little tree which liked the shade and humidity of the great tropical forests: the cacao tree.

And because it was sacred, the pre-Columbian peoples handed down a legend from generation to generation: it told how the precious cacao tree, without which "xocoatl" - later to become "chocolatl"-would not exist, first appeared on Earth.

The origin of the chocolate tree

Topiltzin Quetzalcoatl was a very important person to the Toltecs in the beautiful city of Tula. He was not only their king, but also the high priest of the god of fertility and of the Moon: Quetzalcoatl, the "feathered serpent". His city was rich with treasure: gold, silver, precious green stones... He also gave his people a very special gift: he brought them the cacao tree, the "chocolate tree", from the sacred lands of the first sons of the Sun. One day, three sorcerers who envied his power arrived in Tula. Quetzalcoatl was ill and one of them gave him a potion to drink... but instead of getting better, the King went mad. He left his people and fled to the coast, where he found a raft made of intertwined snakes. He boarded it and disappeared across the sea. But he promised to return one day, in a "year of the reed" on their calendar...

The Prophet Quetzalcoatl from "Quatre siècles d'histoire du Cacao et du Chocolat", Albert Bourgaux (published by the Office International du Cacao et du Chocolat, 1935. Michel Cluizel Collection

Cocoa beans, the Aztec currency

It was probably the soft flesh inside the large fruit of the cacao tree, the cocoa pod, that men, like animals, first enjoyed eating. When did they discover the secret virtues of its seed (or bean)? Who had the idea of cultivating this forest tree in the first place? Hunahpu, the third King of the Mayas, seems to have made cacao growing a decisive factor in the economy, well before the arrival of the Spanish.

Money...

The Aztecs, like the Mayas, used cocoa beans as money. Probably because they were rare and kept well. As a unit of currency, they avoided the difficulties of bartering. A rabbit cost 10 beans, a slave 100... When transactions involved larger objects, another unit was used: the carga. A carga contained 24,000 beans, the maximum weight which could be carried on a man's back. It was the unit used by the enslaved provinces to pay tribute to their masters.

... you could eat

The Aztecs drank their money in the form of a highly spiced drink: "What excellent coin, which provides man with an agreeable food and protects him from the truly infernal curse of avarice", marvelled a Spaniard in 1530. They crushed the beans and grilled them on hot stones: they had discovered that roasting released the flavours of the cocoa. Once they had made the cocoa paste, they mixed it with chilli, pepper, vanilla, etc., added water, and heated the mixture. They then whipped it up until it formed a dense froth, and drank this liquid they called "xocoatl" cold. They valued it all the more as they attributed tonic and aphrodisiac qualities to it.

Cocoa paste was almost certainly also used by the pre-Columbian peoples to heal wounds and cure snakebites.

Cocoa beans

The cocoa pod, fruit of the cacao tree.

The Spanish and the New World

In the 15th century, the Portuguese and the Spanish rivalled each other in audacity to find a new route to the Indies, the fabulous land of spices. Christopher Columbus, an Italian from Genoa, set sail in 1492, sponsored by the Spanish monarchs. When he landed in the West Indies, he thought he had reached Asia - or was he perhaps looking at an earthly Paradise? During his fourth expedition, in 1502, the inspired adventurer was to make another error of judgement: when he moored off the Managua peninsula, a boatload of natives came to meet him and presented him with gifts, including some cocoa beans that Columbus ignored.

Seventeen years later, in 1519, the Spanish conquistador Hernan Cortes landed in Mexico with a fleet of 700 men and 11 ships. He was determined to make his fortune: gold, silver, and spices were the objects of his desire. 1519 was a "year of the reed" in the Aztec calendar: when they saw this pale-skinned man from across the sea, who rode a "giant deer" (a horse), the Aztecs thought that Quetzalcoatl had returned!

A drink worth its weight in gold

The Aztec Emperor Montezuma gave the Spanish conquistadors a lavish welcome in his city, Tenochtitlan, built in the centre of a lake (what is now Mexico City). He had them served with the same frothy, bitter and spicy drink that he drank himself from a cup of the finest gold. Cortes, to whom the Emperor gave a cacao tree plantation, observed that chocolate "builds up resistance and fights fatigue". Even though his compatriots did not really like the taste, they got into the habit of drinking it, as there was no wine to be had. In 1521, Montezuma died and the Aztec empire was renamed New Spain, with Cortes as its all-powerful governor. He showed great foresight: the cocoa bean, used both as money and for making the drink enjoyed by the Aztec nobility, undoubtedly represented a fortune for Spain in general and for him in particular.

Montezuma swears allegiance before Cortes as a subject of the King of Spain.
Lauros-Giraudon (Museum of the Americas, Madrid).

AT THE END OF THE 15TH CENTURY, CHRISTOPHER COLUMBUS LANDED IN THE WEST INDIES, THINKING HE HAD SAILED TO ASIA.

ON HIS 4TH EXPEDITION, IN 1502, HE DROPPED ANCHOR OFF THE MANAGUA PENINSULA, WHERE THE NATIVES PRESENTED HIM WITH MANY GIFTS.

THESE GIFTS OF WELCOME INCLUDED COCOA BEANS, BUT COLUMBUS DID NOT THINK ANYTHING OF THEM.
"GET RID OF THOSE THINGS; THROW THEM OVERBOARD!"

... HE SAILED BACK TO SPAIN, COMPLETELY UNAWARE THAT WHAT HE HAD DISCARDED SO UNCEREMONIOUSLY WAS IN FACT 'CHOCOLATE!'

IN 1519 CORTES LANDED IN MEXICO. THAT YEAR HAPPENED TO BE THE 'YEAR OF THE REED' IN THE AZTEC CALENDAR. HE WAS WELCOMED AS A GOD.

QUETZALCOALT

QUETZALCOALT

HE DRANK THE STRANGE BEVERAGE KNOWN AS 'XOCOATL' AND FOUND IT HAD MANY BENEFICIAL EFFECTS.

FIVE YEARS LATER, CORTES WAS THE HEAD OF THE AZTEC EMPIRE. HE SENT A CARGO OF COCOA BEANS TO SPAIN. THAT'S IT. NOW YOU'RE GOING TO SLEEP, YOUNG MAN. AND I'LL TELL YOU THE REST OF THE STORY OF CHOCOLATE IN EUROPE TOMORROW MORNING.

From the Spanish Court to the whole of Europe

Spain had taken control of part of the New World, so it was via Spanish shores that chocolate reached the Old World. In 1524, Cortes sent a cargo of beans to Emperor Charles V. A few years later, he himself brought the recipe for chocolate to his country. But the addition of sugar, together with honey, vanilla or cinnamon, quickly transformed the Aztecs' bitter brew into a drink full of sweetness. What caused such decisive change?

Cocoa and sugar cane

The first Spanish colonists who settled in America brought with them sugar cane, a native plant of India. Hoping to make their fortunes, they established large numbers of sugar cane and cocoa plantations. One day the two products, so exotic to European eyes, came together, perhaps thanks to the culinary experiments conducted in the monasteries. Cocoa and sugar: modern chocolate was born. However, they still had to perfect the techniques required to make it, and improve the product even more, something chocolate makers to the present day have been constantly striving to achieve.

A career at Court

It was the start of an extraordinary craze at the Spanish Court. Everyone swore by the new drink. The ladies of the court even had it served to them in church! In 1569, following a long debate, Pope Pius V declared that chocolate, like wine, could be drunk during fasting. Soon the whole of Europe was engulfed by the 'brown gold rush'. The recipe could not stay secret for long. The Italians discovered it in 1606, the French in 1615, the Germans in 1642, and the English in 1657. People no longer had to be Spanish to enjoy chocolate, they simply had to be rich.

For their part, European doctors were interested in the curative properties of chocolate. They claimed it cured fevers and stomach aches! In 1736 the Swedish naturalist Carl von Linné christened cocoa Theobroma: "food of the gods". How better to celebrate its many qualities?

A 15th-century Spanish caravel
C. Columbus, Regnù Hyspanie, Basel, 1493.

THE FOLLOWING MORNING

'MORNING, MICHEL. I HOPE YOU DIDN'T DREAM TOO MUCH OF 'FEATHERED SERPENTS'!

NOT AT ALL, DAD. I WANT TO HEAR MORE... YOU PROMISED, DAD... YOU DID..

ALL RIGHT, THEN. REMEMBER: I LEFT THE STORY WHERE CORTES HAD TAKEN OVER THE NEW WORLD. THE SPANISH SETTLERS PLANTED MORE AND MORE CACAO TREES...

AND IT WAS NOT LONG BEFORE THEY STARTED ADDING SUGAR AND HONEY TO THE COCOA, COMPLETELY TRANSFORMING THE BITTER SPICY DRINK. THEY EVEN ADDED VANILLA AND CINAMMON.

... IN SPAIN, IT BECAME A FAVOURITE WITH EVERYBODY AT COURT... THE LADIES HAD IT SERVED IN CHURCH.

POPE PIUS V EVEN DECLARED THAT DRINKING CHOCOLATE WAS NOT AGAINST THE RULES OF FASTING..

'BROWN GOLD' QUICKLY SPREAD THROUGHOUT EUROPE ...

...REACHING ITALY IN 1606

...GERMANY IN 1642

...AND ENGLAND IN 1657

Chocolate arrives in France

Alliances between royal families helped chocolate to enter the court of the King of France. In 1615, Anne of Austria, daughter of Philip III of Spain, married Louis XIII. She was 14. She brought with her a liking for the drink of the Aztecs. In her letters, the Marquise de Sévigné was an enthusiastic ambassadress for chocolate, even though she sometimes ascribed the most terrible powers to it, such as causing a child to be born black and sickly .... Love of good food and medical concerns combined: the Cardinal of Lyons, brother of Cardinal Richelieu, considered chocolate to be "a means of moderating the vapours of the spleen and of combating choler and bad humours".

Commercial trading of chocolate began. In 1659, the young Louis XIV gave David Chaillou, who kept a shop in Rue de l'Arbre Sec in Paris, a 29-year licence granting him the exclusive right to manufacture and sell a "certain composition known as chocolate (...) throughout the Kingdom", whether in liquid or solid form.

Cacao trees on French soil

History repeats itself: in 1661 Marie-Thérèse of Austria, the Spanish Infanta and daughter of Philip IV, married Louis XIV. One historian wrote "The King and chocolate were Marie-Thérèse's only two passions...". But the monarch had no such passion, for neither his wife nor chocolate, even though he did have it served at Versailles. He was aware, however, of its commercial importance and had the cacao tree acclimatised in his West Indian possessions during the 1660s. This meant he was no longer dependent on Spanish supplies. In 1679, with great ceremony, the first harvest from Martinique was landed in Brest.

In 1680 an even more symbolic baptism occurred: the word "chocolat" appeared in Richelet's French dictionary, *Dictionnaire français contenant les mots et les choses*. The Aztecs' "xocoatl" had passed into the French language.

Chocolate remained a privilege of the aristocracy and the clergy until the 18th century. Its consumption gradually became more widespread but this expansion was slowed by the French Revolution and then by the blockades against Napoleon Bonaparte.

Engraving taken from the Traitez nouveaux et curieux du Café, du Thé, du Chocolat, *by Philippe Sylvestre Dufour (1685). Michel Cluizel Collection*

CHOCOLATE WAS INTRODUCED TO FRANCE THROUGH ALLIANCES BETWEEN THE VARIOUS ROYAL FAMILIES.

IN 1615 ANNE OF AUSTRIA, THE DAUGHTER OF KING PHILIP III OF SPAIN, MARRIED KING LOUIS XIII OF FRANCE. SHE WAS 14 AND SHE WAS CRAZY ABOUT CHOCOLATE...

YES, MY DEAR, THE "AZTECS' BEVERAGE". LET'S DRINK IT EVERY DAY...

IT'S ABSOLUTELY DIVINE!

IN 1659 YOUNG KING LOUIS XIV GRANTED DAVID CHAILLOU A ROYAL CHARTER ENABLING HIM TO TRADE IN COCOA.

... YOU ALONE ARE NOW ENTITLED TO MANUFACTURE AND SELL THE CONCOCTION KNOWN AS 'CHOCOLATE'!

THE SUN KING QUICKLY UNDERSTOOD THE IMPORTANCE OF THE COCOA TRADE.

... WE SHALL GROW THIS TREE IN OUR POSSESSIONS IN THE WEST INDIES.

SHORTLY AFTERWARDS, IN 1679, THE FIRST HARVEST FROM MARTINIQUE WAS UNLOADED IN BREST IN GREAT CEREMONY.

IN 1680 THE WORD 'CHOCOLATE' ENTERED RICHELET'S DICTIONARY OF THE FRENCH LANGUAGE.

THE DRINK WAS KNOWN ONLY TO THE CHURCH AND THE ARISTOCRACY TILL THE 18TH CENTURY. ITS SPREAD TO THE PEOPLE AT LARGE WAS SLOW, AND WAS HINDERED BY THE FRENCH REVOLUTION (LATE 1700S) AND THE BLOCKADES AGAINST NAPOLEON (EARLY 1800S).

From craft to industry

The first chocolate makers were apothecaries. Even more than the Aztecs had, they ascribed extraordinary healing powers to this gift of the New World. So it was logical that they should use it in their medicinal preparations.

However, from the 18th century onwards, and within less than two hundred years, the manufacture of chocolate changed from a small-scale craft to an industry, from the back rooms of the early pharmacists to impeccable factories.

Until the mid-19th century, chocolate was mainly consumed as a drink, although it was already available in solid form. In the mid-18th century, food-lovers could enjoy bite-size pieces of chocolate, either plain or topped with hazelnut, pistachio, or small coloured sugar balls. During the same period, "chocolate [was used] for making ... medallions and busts in moulds". These moulds were probably made of pewter, similar to ice-cream moulds. It was not until 1830 that tin moulds appeared.

Ingenious inventors

From the end of the 18th century, in Spain, France, Italy, England, Holland and, later, Switzerland, men worked to mechanise the manufacture of chocolate.

In France in 1778, François Doret presented an invention to the Faculty of Medicine: the first hydraulic machine for grinding cocoa. In 1819 Pelletier built the first steam-driven chocolate factory in Rue Richelieu in Paris. The same year, in Switzerland, François Louis Cailler returned home after working for four years in the Caffarel chocolate factory in Turin; he commissioned

the construction of a grinder to his own design which ground cocoa and sugar between two horizontal rollers turning towards each other.

Italian worker in a Turin "Cioccolateria" (1859).

APOTHECARIES WERE THE FIRST CHOCOLATE MAKERS... EVEN MORE THAN THE AZTECS, THEY CLAIMED THAT CHOCOLATE COULD CURE ALL SORTS OF AILMENTS AND ILLNESSES, AND THEY USED IT IN THEIR ELIXIRS ...

CHOCOLATE WAS ONLY A DRINK FOR QUITE A LONG TIME, BUT THERE WAS A ALSO A SOLID VERSION OF IT...

FROM THE MIDDLE OF THE 18TH CENTURY ONWARDS PEOPLE COULD ENJOY BITE-SIZED CHOCOLATE PIECES, EITHER PLAIN OR TOPPED WITH HAZELNUTS, PISTACHIOS OR SUGAR BALLS.

... CAST IN PEWTER MOULDS, CHOCOLATE WAS TURNED INTO MEDALLIONS OR BUSTS...

IT WAS NOT LONG BEFORE THE MAKING OF CHOCOLATE WOULD BECOME AN INDUSTRY: IN LESS THAN TWO CENTURIES, CHOCOLATE WOULD LEAVE THE BACK ROOMS OF THE APOTHECARIES AND MOVE TO IMPECCABLE FACTORIES.

In 1829 the Gazette of the period mentions that S. Debauve, a former pharmacist to Louis XVI and his nephew A. Gallais, chocolate makers in Paris, designed a machine for grinding and kneading chocolate in their workshop. This machine consisted of two marble rollers turning on a granite base. Two machines based on this principle are still used in Michel Cluizel's factory for certain products. One can be seen at the Chocolatrium.

The Menier family was one of the great pioneers of the chocolate industry. In 1825 Jean-Antoine Brutus Menier, a pharmacist, opened a chocolate factory in an old mill on the Marne River near Noisiel.

In Switzerland, Daniel Peter fell in love with Fanny Cailler, the daughter of the leading Swiss chocolate maker, and found his vocation. In 1875 he invented milk chocolate using the milk condensation process which had just been developed by Henri Nestlé.

At the end of the 19th century, Rodolphe Lindt discovered the value of working chocolate for long periods in a longitudinal "kneader" or conching machine. This prolonged period of conching is still being used for quality chocolate as it eliminates the bitter and acid odours and flavours naturally contained in cocoa beans.

Chocolates

It was around the same time that the first chocolates appeared. In France the product is known as a "bonbon de chocolat" (literally "chocolate sweet") while in Germany it is called a "praline".

At that time the centre was almost certainly made of fondant (cooked and beaten sugar which formed a soft white paste, ready for colouring or flavouring). This fondant had to be shaped into a ball in the palms of the hands. The worker then placed it on a marble table, coated (or enrobed) it with chocolate using three fingers and placed it on a sheet of paper. To complete his work, he used his index finger to draw the chocolate up into a decorative spiral twist. It is probably the shape of this decoration which has led to the name "chocolate whirl".

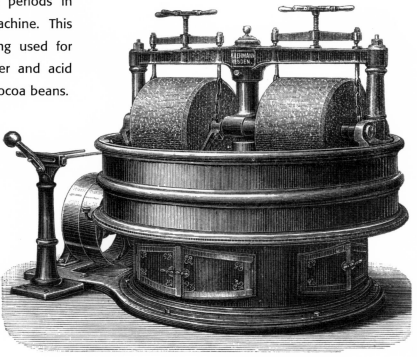

Grinder with granite rollers and base, used for conching. Machine used by Michel Cluizel during his apprenticeship and on which he made his first couverture chocolate.

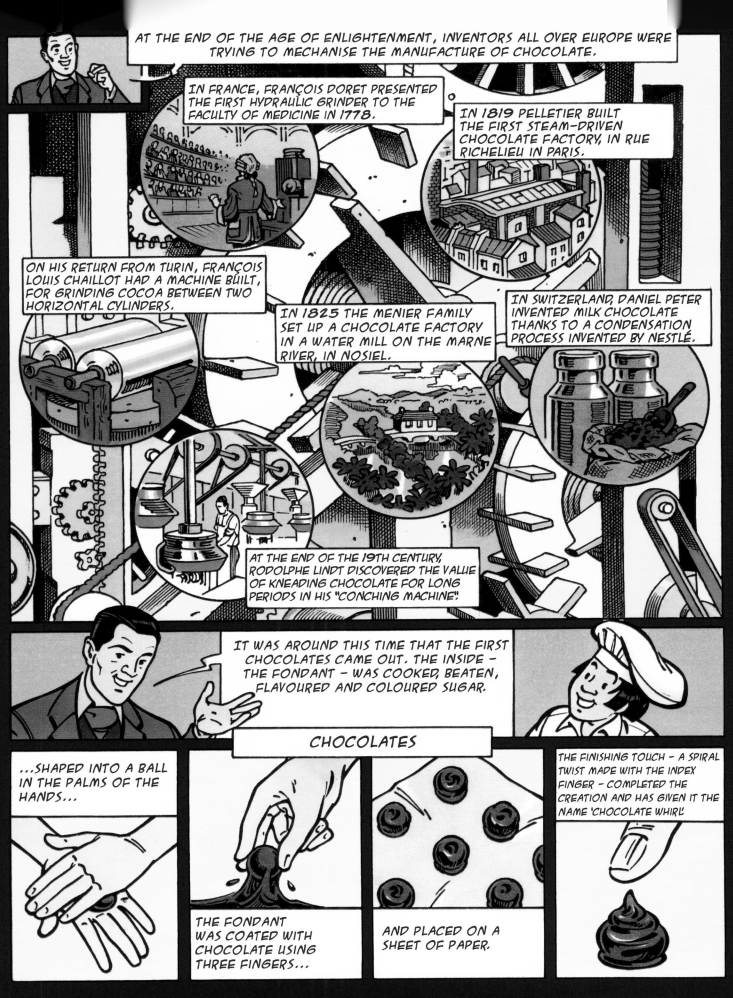

AT THE END OF THE AGE OF ENLIGHTENMENT, INVENTORS ALL OVER EUROPE WERE TRYING TO MECHANISE THE MANUFACTURE OF CHOCOLATE.

IN FRANCE, FRANÇOIS DORET PRESENTED THE FIRST HYDRAULIC GRINDER TO THE FACULTY OF MEDICINE IN 1778.

IN 1819 PELLETIER BUILT THE FIRST STEAM-DRIVEN CHOCOLATE FACTORY, IN RUE RICHELIEU IN PARIS.

ON HIS RETURN FROM TURIN, FRANÇOIS LOUIS CHAILLOT HAD A MACHINE BUILT, FOR GRINDING COCOA BETWEEN TWO HORIZONTAL CYLINDERS.

IN 1825 THE MENIER FAMILY SET UP A CHOCOLATE FACTORY IN A WATER MILL ON THE MARNE RIVER, IN NOSIEL.

IN SWITZERLAND, DANIEL PETER INVENTED MILK CHOCOLATE THANKS TO A CONDENSATION PROCESS INVENTED BY NESTLÉ.

AT THE END OF THE 19TH CENTURY, RODOLPHE LINDT DISCOVERED THE VALUE OF KNEADING CHOCOLATE FOR LONG PERIODS IN HIS "CONCHING MACHINE"!

IT WAS AROUND THIS TIME THAT THE FIRST CHOCOLATES CAME OUT. THE INSIDE – THE FONDANT – WAS COOKED, BEATEN, FLAVOURED AND COLOURED SUGAR.

CHOCOLATES

...SHAPED INTO A BALL IN THE PALMS OF THE HANDS...

THE FONDANT WAS COATED WITH CHOCOLATE USING THREE FINGERS...

AND PLACED ON A SHEET OF PAPER.

THE FINISHING TOUCH – A SPIRAL TWIST MADE WITH THE INDEX FINGER – COMPLETED THE CREATION AND HAS GIVEN IT THE NAME 'CHOCOLATE WHIRL'.

Dipping forks used by Michel Cluizel during his apprenticeship

In about 1920 chocolate makers began to abandon the practice of using their fingers to enrobe chocolates and instead dipped them using small tools made of metal wire known as "forks" due to the shape of one kind. Having first "tempered" the chocolate (seeding of solid chocolate in hot liquid chocolate), the chocolate maker used a fork to dip the "centre" of the chocolate into liquid chocolate, then lifted it out, drained it and placed it on a sheet of paper. He then used the fork to make a line pattern on the chocolate. Very few chocolate makers still use this process, although manual decoration is still imitated.

Industrial developments in the 20th century

During the first half of the 20th century, the major family-run chocolate manufacturers, in France and elsewhere, expanded and their machinery continued to evolve.

In 1903 a French chocolate maker, Magniez, invented a machine for enrobing chocolates. The centres passed through a curtain of liquid chocolate which covered them. The machine known as an "enrober" was born.

After the Second World War, it was the Germans who improved the machinery used for chocolate in general. Robert Sollich and his son Helmut invented a machine for tempering chocolate, which revolutionised the process. He then adapted the tempering machine to include enrobing. In 1965 the first automatic enrober and temperer to be delivered in France was installed in the Cluizel family's small factory.

Two 40-metre-long enrobing lines - still the Sollich brand - can be found in Michel Cluizel's factory today.

TOWARDS 1920 CHOCOLATES WERE NO LONGER COATED MANUALLY, AND THIS TOOL STARTED TO BE USED FOR DIPPING....

CHOCOLATE MAKERS DIPPED THE CENTRE OR FILLING INTO A BOWL OF CHOCOLATE....

LIFTED IT OUT AND DRAINED IT...

THEN THEY PUT IT ON PAPER AND USED THE FORK TO MAKE A PATTERN IN THE CHOCOLATE...

IN THE FIRST HALF OF THE 20TH CENTURY THE FAMOUS FAMILY-RUN CHOCOLATE FACTORIES DEVELOPED, IN FRANCE AND ABROAD, AND MACHINES EVOLVED ...

1903. MAGNIEZ INVENTED A MACHINE FOR COATING CHOCOLATES.

1903

1965. THE FIRST AUTOMATIC COATER AND TEMPERER TO BE DELIVERED IN FRANCE WAS INSTALLED IN THE CLUIZEL CHOCOLATE FACTORY.

1965

Double-line modern enrober in Michel Cluizel's factory

Most medium-sized manufacturers now have machinery enabling them to produce chocolate bars and chocolates of very high quality provided they have the required expertise and use the best possible raw materials. Michel Cluizel's chocolate factory combines both these qualities.

Early 20ᵗʰ-century enrober

A CHOCOLATE PRODUCTION LINE IN THE CLUIZEL CHOCOLATE FACTORY.

Cultivating the cacao tree

For an exceptional product, an exceptional tree. The strangely-shaped cacao tree has to be pampered to obtain the treasures hidden in its fruit, the "pods".

The tree produces dense foliage and bears flowers and fruits at the same time, an exceptional botanical phenomenon. All year round, in fact, it produces small clusters of white flowers directly on its trunk and the main branches. Only one in every hundred flowers produces a fruit (or pod): the small flies which pollinate it only have a few hours to work. Even then nothing is guaranteed: 20% of the fruit dies before it ripens.

The pods are as impressive as the flowers are fragile. Oval in shape, they measure between 15 and 25 cm in length. On a single tree some young pods may be yellow, green or almost violet, others, ready for picking, range from yellow to almost orange. Inside the fruit, under the thick skin, lies a white pulp called the mucilage and almond-shaped seeds or beans (20 to 40 per fruit). These beans contain the precious cocoa.

Cacao tree blossoms, 1 cm in diameter

A delicate tree

In order to blossom and bear fruit, the cacao tree needs to be planted at a latitude between 20° north and 20° south, and for many years it was grown only in the Americas. In 1822 it was established in Africa.

It requires a hot climate, around 28°C, not too much wind, shade - palm trees provide the right amount - and a good but not excessive level of moisture.

It grows to an average height of 3 to 8 metres in plantations, where it is pruned, but can exceed 12 metres in the wild. A cacao tree flowers at four years old, reaches maturity at 12 years of age, and remains productive for about thirty years.

Cacao tree with its fruit, the 'pods'.

DO YOU WANT TO UNDERSTAND WHAT COCOA IS? COME ON THEN, COME WITH ME TO THE FACTORY...

THERE YOU ARE. IN THIS ROOM YOU'LL FIND EVERYTHING YOU WANT TO FIND OUT ABOUT THE PLANT, THE FRUIT, THE SEED...

THAT'S CHOCOLATE, THEN, IS IT?

THAT'S RIGHT. THAT'S THE BEAN, AND IT COMES FROM AN AMAZING TREE... THE CACAO TREE.

Cacao tree

IT CAN ONLY BE GROWN IN TROPICAL COUNTRIES, IN THE LATITUDES BETWEEN 20°C NORTH AND 20°C SOUTH, BECAUSE IT NEEDS A TEMPERATURE OF APPROXIMATELY 28°C.

THE TREE IS 3 TO 8 METRES HIGH, ON AVERAGE, AND IT BLOSSOMS WHEN IT IS 4 YEARS OLD. ITS FLOWERS MAKE IT AN EXCEPTIONAL TREE ...

Ecuador

Cacao tree

...FOR IT BLOSSOMS AND BEARS FRUIT AT THE SAME TIME. ITS FRUIT GROWS STRAIGHT FROM THE TRUNK.

ONLY ONE FLOWER IN A HUNDRED GIVES FRUIT AND THE SMALL FLIES THAT POLLINATE IT HAVE TO WORK FAST: THEY ONLY HAVE A FEW HOURS TO DO THEIR JOB....

AND EVEN THEN IT'S NOT OVER, FOR 20% OF THE FRUIT DIES BEFORE IT IS RIPE.

SEE THIS FRUIT? IT'S THE POD.

IT'S BETWEEN 15 AND 25 CM LONG.

INSIDE, UNDER THE THICK SKIN, LIES A WHITE PULP AND SOME SEEDS...

OR BEANS. THESE BEANS ARE WHAT GIVES US THE PRECIOUS COCOA.

The cocoa bean

The road from bean to chocolate is a long one. This is easily demonstrated by tasting a bean freshly removed from its pod: its bitter fragrance, heavy with tannin, bears no resemblance to the refined treat we so enjoy. This long road starts in the plantation...

After 5 to 6 months, the pod is ripe and makes a hollow sound when gently tapped. It is carefully cut from the tree, by hand or by pole, so as not to damage the tree's delicate bark. Then the plantation worker splits it open with a single blow of a stout stick or machete and reveals the precious beans.

The beans are removed from the pulp. They are put into piles and covered with banana leaves to promote a natural chemical reaction, fermentation, which brings out their flavours.

The beans are then carefully dried on racks in the sun. After two weeks, they turn a beautiful brown colour. Their moisture content drops from 60% to 8%, ensuring optimum conservation. They are now ready to leave the plantation packed in jute sacks and to make the long voyage to the country where they will be transformed into chocolate.

But the beans will not all go to the same chocolate factories! At Michel Cluizel's, the quality of the finished product begins with the raw materials. This is why the beans are always selected from samples, and not simply on the basis of their origin. In the age-old tradition of the great craftsmen, Michel Cluizel and his son Marc work together, smelling, handling, and tasting the beans. If the quality is good enough, they place an order. On its arrival, the merchandise will be inspected and compared with the reference sample. No question of accepting a "slatey" bean, meaning one which has gone mouldy during fermentation!

Michel Cluizel examining drying beans on a plantation

Forastero pod

Trinitario pod

Criollo pod

26

... BUT IT IS A LONG ROAD FROM THE BEAN TO CHOCOLATE.

TO UNDERSTAND WHAT I MEAN, SIMPLY EAT ONE STRAIGHT FROM THE POD. IT IS HARSH AND BITTER AND DOESN'T TASTE ANYTHING LIKE A CHOCOLATE.

POUAH!

...SO IT HAS TO BE WORKED AND PROCESSED.

A) THE POD IS RIPE AFTER 5 OR 6 MONTHS. ITS COLOUR CHANGES AND IT SOUNDS HOLLOW.

B) IT HAS TO BE CUT FROM THE TREE BY HAND SO THAT THE BARK DOES NOT GET DAMAGED.

C) THE PLANTATION WORKER THEN SPLITS IT OPEN WITH A SINGLE BLOW OF A STOUT STICK OR MACHETE.

D) AND REMOVES THE PRECIOUS SEEDS.

E) WITHIN 24 HOURS OF REMOVAL FROM THE POD, THE SEEDS ARE PILED IN THE SUN AND COVERED UP SO THAT CONTROLLED FERMENTATION CAN ELIMINATE THE MUCILAGE (THE PULP), BRING OUT THE FLAVOURS, AND PREVENT GERMINATION.

... THEY ARE THEN LEFT TO DRY IN THE SUN AND AFTER 2 WEEKS THEY ARE A BEAUTIFUL BROWN COLOUR.

NOW THEY ARE READY TO BE DELIVERED TO CHOCOLATE FACTORIES. IT IS AT THIS STAGE THAT THE BEANS ARE SELECTED, FOR THERE ARE THREE DIFFERENT TYPES OF CACAO TREE.

CRIOLLOS: SWEET AROMATIC BEANS. EXPENSIVE BECAUSE THEY COME IN SMALL QUANTITIES.

FORASTEROS: THE TREE PRODUCES MORE, BUT THE QUALITY IS LOWER.

TRINITARIOS: A HYBRID OF THE OTHER TWO, ACCOUNTS FOR MOST OF THE WORLD'S PRODUCTION.

From purchasing to conching

Like sugar or gold, cocoa from three continents is quoted on the commodities exchanges in New York and London. Its price is subject to fluctuation based on supply, demand and trading forecasts. For this reason, Michel Cluizel has to be not only an expert on cocoa, but also a stock market expert: he has to decide when the rate is right for buying, to give his customers the best possible price.

At the same time as their value is fluctuating, the beans are embarking on a slower trip of transformation. The best varieties, the ones sought by Michel Cluizel, are sorted and graded. Then, instead of being stored in large silos as happens with the big industrial producers, they are kept in rows of jute sacks, which, by enabling constant ventilation, prevent any danger of overheating. In the production areas at the Cluizel factory, the chocolate makers are about to start work...

The stages in the magic process

After elimination of the last impurities, the beans move into an ultra-modern roaster which guarantees perfectly even roasting right through the bean, using two complementary heating techniques. The aroma develops, the last traces of moisture disappear, the thin husk falls away.

The husks and seed germs are removed during cracking. Only the bean or "nib" remains, the best part of the cocoa bean, which will continue through the long series of processes required to make chocolate.

Once the beans have been ground into a paste, Michel Cluizel blends one or more cocoas of different origins, which have complementary flavour qualities, in a kneader. Cane sugar and Bourbon vanilla pods are also added at this stage, as well as milk when making milk chocolate.

After double grinding, this paste becomes fine and even, guaranteeing a chocolate which melts in the mouth.

Conching, a kneading action which oxygenates the cocoa mass, is carefully calculated to evaporate the bitter and acid flavours which cocoa naturally contains. This stage also enables the aromas to fully develop and gives the chocolate its beautiful glossy appearance. At Michel Cluizel's, the age-old tradition of craftsmen and modern technology combine harmoniously to improve performance: the conching machines are the latest generation, and adapt to the paste as the operation progresses, to bring out the best in the chocolate.

JUST LIKE SUGAR OR GOLD, COCOA IS QUOTED ON THE INTERNATIONAL COMMODITIES MARKETS.

... ITS PRICE IS SUBJECT TO FLUCTUATION BASED ON SUPPLY AND DEMAND. IT IS THEREFORE IMPORTANT TO BUY WHEN THE PRICE IS MOST ADVANTAGEOUS, AND THUS BE ABLE TO PRODUCE AFFORDABLE CHOCOLATE.

UNLIKE THE BIG MANUFACTURERS, WE STORE THE BEANS WE HAVE SELECTED–THE VERY FINEST–IN JUTE SACKS, SINCE THIS ENABLES CONSTANT VENTILATION AND PREVENTS FERMENTATION.

THEN COMES THE TIME FOR THE ALCHEMY OF CHOCOLATE MAKING TO WORKS ITS FIVE CRUCIAL STAGES

1 ROASTING: AFTER REMOVAL OF IMPURITIES, THE BEANS ARE ROASTED TO PERFECTION IN AN INFRA-RED ROASTER.

2 CRUSHING: THIS OPERATION BREAKS THE BEANS INTO TINY PIECES AND REMOVES THE SHELLS AND SEED GERMS.

3 A BALL GRINDER THEN GRINDS THE BEAN FRAGMENTS WHICH TURN LIQUID IN THE HEAT.

4 BLENDING AND REFINING: THE COCOA LIQUOR IS BLENDED WITH SUGAR (AND EVEN MILK) AND REFINED TO 18 MICROMETRE SIZE BETWEEN STEEL ROLLERS*.

5 CONCHING HEATS, KNEADS AND OXYGENATES THE COCOA MASS TO ELIMINATE ITS NATURAL SHARP FLAVOURS.

*SEE WORKSHOP, PAGE 23

Different sorts of chocolate

Several basic products are derived from the roasted beans. Mechanical grinding of the beans produces cocoa paste. In their raw state, the beans contain approximately 55% cocoa butter. Hydraulic presses put this paste under very high pressure which separates out the melted cocoa butter, the most precious material, from the cake, which is the dry part.

Successively crushed, pulverised and sieved, the press cake produces pure cocoa powder, used in the preparation of chocolate drinks and desserts.

The chocolate industry is highly regulated. Each product is defined by law, based on its cocoa content and the other ingredients used. For example, distinctions are made between dark chocolate, milk chocolate, couverture chocolate, boxed chocolates, etc. It is then up to chocolate makers to outdo each other by offering gourmets exceptional flavours. It is to this that Michel Cluizel's company is dedicated.

The best raw materials

At Michel Cluizel's, distinct cocoas and all other ingredients are selected on the basis of the most severe criteria. Is that not the essential guarantee of quality? Dark chocolate requires paste from the best cocoa beans: some of Michel Cluizel's chocolate bars are composed of a mixture of nine different cocoas to achieve a perfect and complete aromatic balance; for a more characteristic flavour and aroma, others use just one "pure origin" cocoa from a single place. Pure coarse cane sugar and Bourbon vanilla pods are also required: no question

here of replacing genuine vanilla with vanillin, a cheap synthetic product. No question either of adding cocoa powder to the chocolate, a practice which enables a higher cocoa content to be achieved at a lower cost.

As well as a wide range of finished products, Michel Cluizel manufactures a couverture chocolate whose reputation is unparalleled. Leading restaurants and pastry chefs use it for enrobing and decorating their creations.

At the beginning of the year 2000, Michel Cluizel stopped using soy lecithin in the manufacture of all his chocolates (dark, milk, white and coloured); this is the only means of guaranteeing they are all 100% GM-free.

Chocolates

What is a chocolate? An exquisite treat which hides a centre full of surprises under its chocolate coating. But what ingredients go to make up this interior? They are few in number: almonds, hazelnuts, walnuts, pistachios, raisins, vanilla, cream, butter, sugar, coffee, liqueurs, cherries in kirsch. Using this selection, the chocolate maker's art lies in endlessly creating new flavours, born of unexpected blends. Unlike other chocolate makers, Michel Cluizel has always refused to give pride of place to ganache, which, despite its good reputation, cannot fully express the opulence of chocolates. Each creation is the result of skilful alchemy: like wine, chocolate is a complex material, almost a living being.

"The best products require the best raw materials" Michel Cluizel.

Choosing the best

Michel Cluizel insists on the best products, whether for the centre or the topping of his chocolates. Whether they are visible or not is not a criterion! The raw material used must be of the highest quality. It is processed within the factory to ensure stable and optimum quality. Cherries and raisins are left to mature in kirsch and marc brandies for at least a year, in oak casks in a cellar at the chocolate factory. Similarly, only plump and graded whole hazelnuts and almonds are selected, even if they are to be used ground. These are delivered once a year, straight from the harvest, and not intermittently, as required, as is usually the case. They are stored at a constant level of humidity and a temperature of 8 - 9°C. This ensures they are stored in perfect condition and do not oxidise.

But which nuts does Michel Cluizel treat with so much care? The very best, naturally. For praline: Italian hazelnuts from the Rome area, whose flavour remains stable for long periods. For gianduja: Piedmont hazelnuts, the very best. For almond paste and praline: Spanish almonds whose flesh is tender and oily, which is not the case with those from other sources.

To make his chocolates even more delicious, Michel Cluizel keeps them quite small. They cost more to produce, because the same operations are needed for a greater number of units, but their enjoyment is increased tenfold.

Let us take a look at how Michel Cluizel creates the wonderful preparations designed for the centres of his chocolates....

A LARGE PROPORTION OF ALL THE CHOCOLATE PRODUCED IS USED TO MAKE INDIVIDUAL OR BOXED CHOCOLATES. THERE IS A TREMENDOUS RANGE OF TYPES.

THE CENTRE OR FILLING OF CHOCOLATES IS SOMETIMES REFERRED TO AS THE 'INTERIOR'.

INTERIORS ARE MADE WITH A RANGE OF DIFFERENT INGREDIENTS: ALMONDS, HAZELNUTS, RAISINS, LIQUEURS...

THE RAW MATERIALS MUST BE THE VERY BEST. WE USE ONLY WHOLE HAZELNUTS AND ALMONDS FROM PLACES WHERE TOP QUALITY IS GUARANTEED.

WITH PISTACHIOS, RAISINS, VANILLA, CREAM, SUGAR, COFFEE, LIQUEURS, AND CHERRIES, CHOCOLATE MAKERS CAN CHOOSE FROM A WHOLE PALETTE OF FLAVOURS TO CREATE EXCITING NEW DELICACIES...

HAZELNUTS

ALMONDS

RAISINS

Praline

The taste of praline combines marvellously with chocolate. Michel Cluizel still makes it the traditional way, as this develops the flavour to the maximum. No question of turning to industrial praline, made with hazelnuts or almonds which are toasted and then ground with white sugar! At Michel Cluizel's, whole almonds and/or hazelnuts are cooked through, in caramelised cane sugar in large copper boilers heated over a naked flame. This cooking method ensures a perfect osmosis between the nuts and the sugar. Once the praline is cooked, it is cooled naturally, to remove any trace of moisture. Following tradition, it is first ground in a granite mill, the only material suitable for grinding this type of product.

Gianduja

Gianduja is Italian: in 1865, during a carnival, the masked Piedmontese character in Commedia dell'Arte plays, Gian d'la Duja (John the Pitcher, a nickname derived from his love for wine) handed out chocolates to the crowd made by the famous Caffarel company. These specialities have borne his name since that day. At Michel Cluizel's, roast Piedmont hazelnuts and cane sugar are worked together with cocoa paste to produce a filling which is smooth and aromatic, a delight on the palate.

The praline is removed from large copper boilers when cooked. (Michel Cluizel chocolate factory)

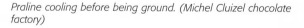

Praline cooling before being ground. (Michel Cluizel chocolate factory)

Grinding praline in the granite mill. (Michel Cluizel chocolate factory)

TO MAKE THE MOST OF ALL THOSE FLAVOURS, CHOCOLATE MAKERS HAVE DESIGNED SPECIAL PREPARATIONS FOR MAKING FILLINGS...

...LET ME TELL YOU ABOUT THE GREAT CLASSICS AND THEIR TRADITIONAL MEANS OF MANUFACTURE HANDED DOWN TO ME BY MY FATHER...

PRALINE

THIS IS ONE SUCH 'TRADITIONAL' PREPARATION. ALMONDS AND HAZELNUTS ARE COOKED IN SUGAR IN LARGE COPPER BASINS OVER NAKED FLAMES.

THE RESULTING PRALINE IS LEFT TO COOL IN THE OPEN AIR BEFORE BEING GROUND BY GRANITE ROLLERS.

GIANDUJA

CAFEAREL

THERE IS A STORY BEHIND GIANDUJA TOO: IN 1865, AT A CARNIVAL IN ITALY, A MASKED CHARACTER IN A PLAY CALLED GIAN D'LA DUJA HANDED OUT CHOCOLATES TO THE CROWD. THEY WERE MADE WITH A CHOCOLATE PASTE, MILK AND FINELY GROUND HAZELNUTS. THIS DELICIOUS CHOCOLATE IS NOW NAMED AFTER HIM.

Nougatine

At Michel Cluizel's, light-brown turbinado sugar and roasted almonds are cooked in a copper mixer, then worked by hand on a bench, before being shaped by bronze rollers. Skilled staff ensure that the paste contains enough almonds to give the nougatine (also called 'croquant') an enjoyably brittle snap.

Almond paste

Almond paste is made of high quality uncooked almonds, blanched and ground with cane sugar. Pistachios from Sicily are sometimes added to provide their subtle flavour and adorn the chocolates with their pretty green colour that is more than a match for Iranian pistachios.

Making of almond paste

Liqueurs

Liqueur chocolates are not easy to make, but they are certainly worth all the trouble. The combination of the chocolate shell and a centre with a perfect liquid texture makes a rare treat for the gourmet palate. The quality of the liqueur depends on a consistently fine sugar crust and on the flavours of the alcohols selected.

Just how is the liquid alcohol trapped inside a solid chocolate shell? Here is the secret of this magic formula... First, hollows are formed in a layer of perfectly dry, sieved starch. The confectioners at the Michel Cluizel chocolate factory pour into them a delicate syrup of sugar and water, made over a naked flame and blended with the selected liqueur. The sugar crystallises naturally and forms a thin crust around the liquid alcohol. Its protective layer of starch can then be removed by meticulous brushing, ready for the chocolate coating.

Cherries stored in brandy in the cellars at the Michel Cluizel chocolate factory.

NOUGATINE

LIGHT-BROWN TURBINADO SUGAR AND PIECES OF ROASTED ALMOND ARE COOKED IN A COPPER MIXER BEFORE BEING WORKED BY HAND AND SHAPED BY BRONZE ROLLERS.

ALMOND PASTE

ALMOND PASTE IS MADE OF HIGH-QUALITY BLANCHED UNCOOKED ALMONDS GROUND WITH CANE SUGAR. PISTACHIOS MAY BE ADDED TO ENHANCE THE FLAVOUR.

FOR CHOCOLATES WITH LIQUID CENTRES, THE RAW MATERIAL IS MADE IN THE CHOCOLATE FACTORY. CHERRIES AND RAISINS ARE MATURED IN KIRSCH AND AGED MARC BRANDY IN OAK CASKS FOR AT LEAST ONE YEAR.

LIQUID CENTRES

HOW CAN A LIQUID BE TRAPPED IN SOLID CHOCOLATE? .... HERE'S THE SECRET OF THIS MAGIC.

HOLLOWS ARE FORMED IN A LAYER OF SIEVED STARCH TO MAKE A MOULD....

THEY ARE FILLED WITH A SYRUP OF SUGAR AND LIQUEUR OR ALCOHOL.

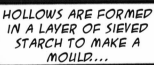

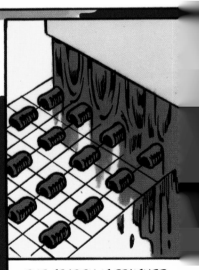

THE SUGAR CRYSTALLISES ON THE OUTSIDE, FORMING A THIN CRUST AROUND THE LIQUID...

THE STARCH IS BRUSHED OFF AND THE 'FILLING' IS COATED WITH CHOCOLATE.

Ganache

Ganache, like "Bêtises de Cambrai" (a type of mint sweet from northern France), was one of those culinary mistakes which turned into a masterpiece.

One day, an apprentice spilt some milk onto the chocolate he was making. His master, furious at his clumsiness, called him a "ganache", the French term for "bungler". As he did not want to waste the mix, he stirred the milk into the chocolate and, to his surprise, the result was a smooth cream. Ganache was born.

Ganache is a sort of thick cream. It is made from chocolate to which a form of fat (fresh cream, butter or a syrup) has been added. It should be smooth, shiny, and of perfectly even consistency, with no graininess. Ganache can be left plain or it can be flavoured. Michel Cluizel requires flavourings to be obtained directly from the product itself: a zest of crystallised orange peel, ground coffee beans, tea infusions or Bourbon vanilla pods. A ganache worthy of the name is delicately flavoured and never cloying.

Caramel

Caramel is made from sugar, butter, milk and glucose syrup. It may also contain ingredients such as dried fruits, nuts, and chocolate or coffee flavouring. To complement the chocolate perfectly, it should be soft without sticking to the teeth.

Nougat

Made from egg whites whipped with sugar syrup, nougat also contains nuts.

The Michel Cluizel chocolate factory manufactures only "Montelimar nougat", a name to which only products of the highest quality are entitled. Its nut filling must comprise exclusively almonds and pistachios, and must account for at least 30% of the weight of the finished product. The sweetening agents used must contain at least 25% honey.

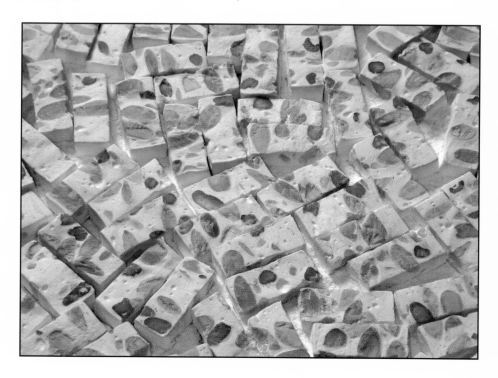

Finishing
the chocolate

Before being used to enrobe a chocolate or being poured into a mould, chocolate must be "tempered"; this means bringing it to a temperature of between 27 and 30 degrees centigrade (depending on whether it is dark or milk chocolate). This process requires considerable expertise, now put into effect by electronically-controlled machines. When tempering is carried out skilfully and the chocolate has been shaped and cooled, it will snap neatly and it will have a smooth and glossy finish which will last a long time under the right storage conditions.

We now have all the ingredients: delicious chocolate and sophisticated centres. Everything is ready for them to mingle their subtle flavours. It is time to design a shape worthy of their taste.

Enrobing

The centres are ready for enrobing. This operation is carried out by a machine called an enrobing line. The centre moves into an enrober which covers it in a fine layer of chocolate. As it comes out of the machine, expert hands decorate each chocolate with the aid of a small metal fork or adorn them with a hazelnut or perhaps a pistachio... Some are even decorated with gold leaf (22.5 carats) or with a piped teardrop or rosette of gianduja, using a truly authentic process. Michel Cluizel favours a balanced ratio between the centre and the coating of a chocolate. This perfect balance follows the tradition developed at a time when chocolates were enrobed by hand or with a fork. The chocolates are ready. They move into a refrigerated "tunnel", where they harden, then go on to small trays where they remain for 24 hours before being placed in boxes for dispatch to confectioners, pastrychefs, or cake shops.

Michel Cluizel supplies branded and non-branded chocolates to some 5,000 bakeries or pastry, confectionery, and cake shops, together with coffee roasters. His chocolates have made the reputation of some of the most celebrated purveyors of fine foods in France and beyond.

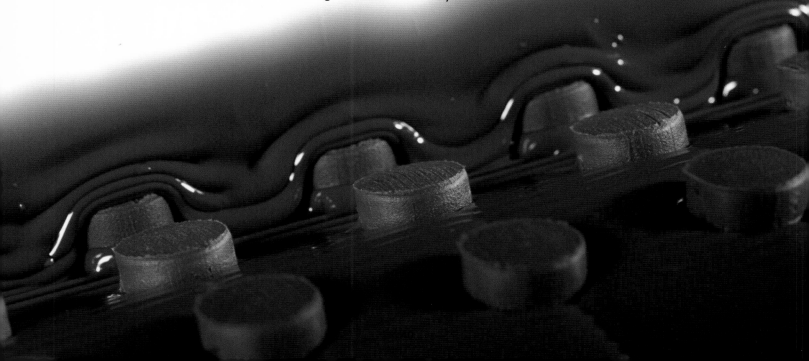

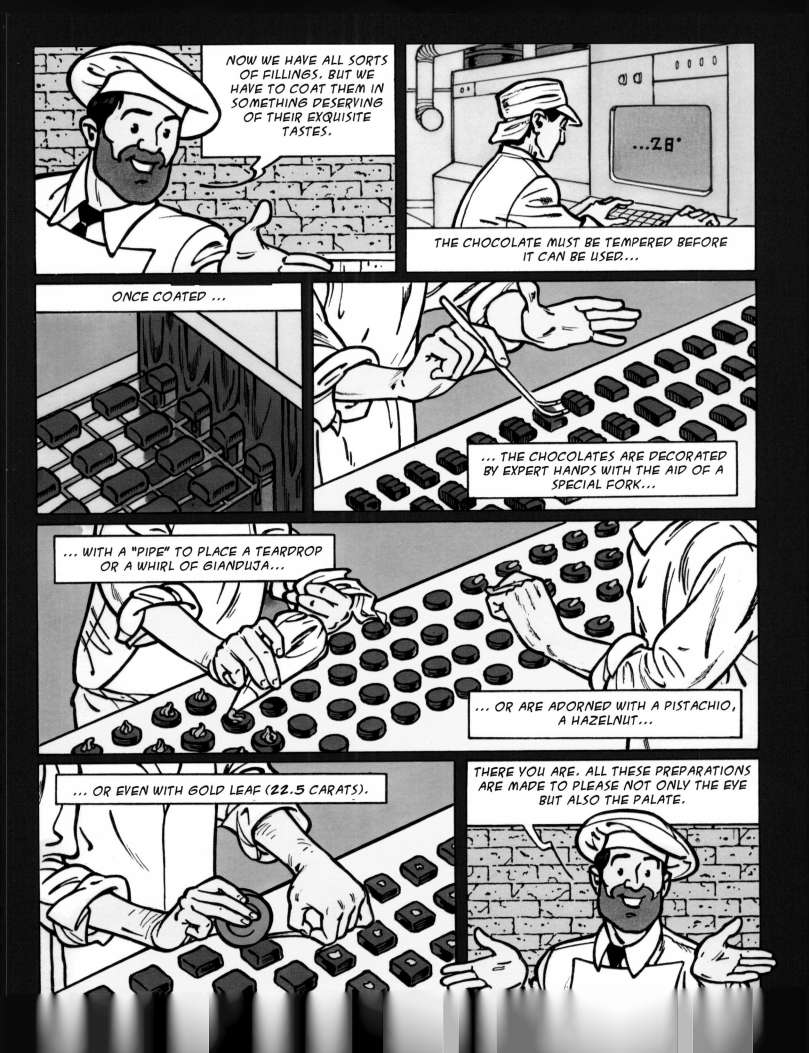

Pan coating

Other noble products are coated with chocolate using the pan coating process. Almonds, coffee beans, cocoa bean nibs or even tiny chocolate eggs filled with praline, are placed in large copper basins. Into these basins, which rotate continuously, turning the centres over and over, are repeatedly poured tiny amounts of liquid chocolate (more than 100 times). The operation takes seven hours and only stops when the centres have been given the correct thickness of chocolate coating. Some are then coated with a fine layer of sugar, like the tiny eggs decorated to look like bird's eggs. Other products are left just with their chocolate covering but the craftsman's skill gives them a perfect gloss finish.

Early moulds.

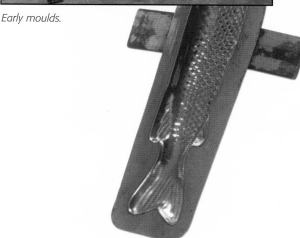

Moulding

Some products are manufactured using a process which is the complete reverse of enrobing and pan coating: the shape of the chocolate is not determined by its centre but by a mould. This process is used in the Michel Cluizel chocolate factory for making products with very soft or semi-liquid centres.

A rigid plastic mould with hollows in the form of a finished chocolate is filled with tempered chocolate. The mould is vibrated to eliminate any air bubbles, then turned over to partially empty the hollows of their content of chocolate. Once the mould has cooled and the chocolate has hardened, the chocolate shell receives its filling. The shell is then capped with a fine layer of chocolate, and the product is ready. The same process is used for making the chocolate shells for Easter eggs, chicks and rabbits, and Halloween pumpkins. Chocolate bars and squares are made in the same sort of moulds.

42

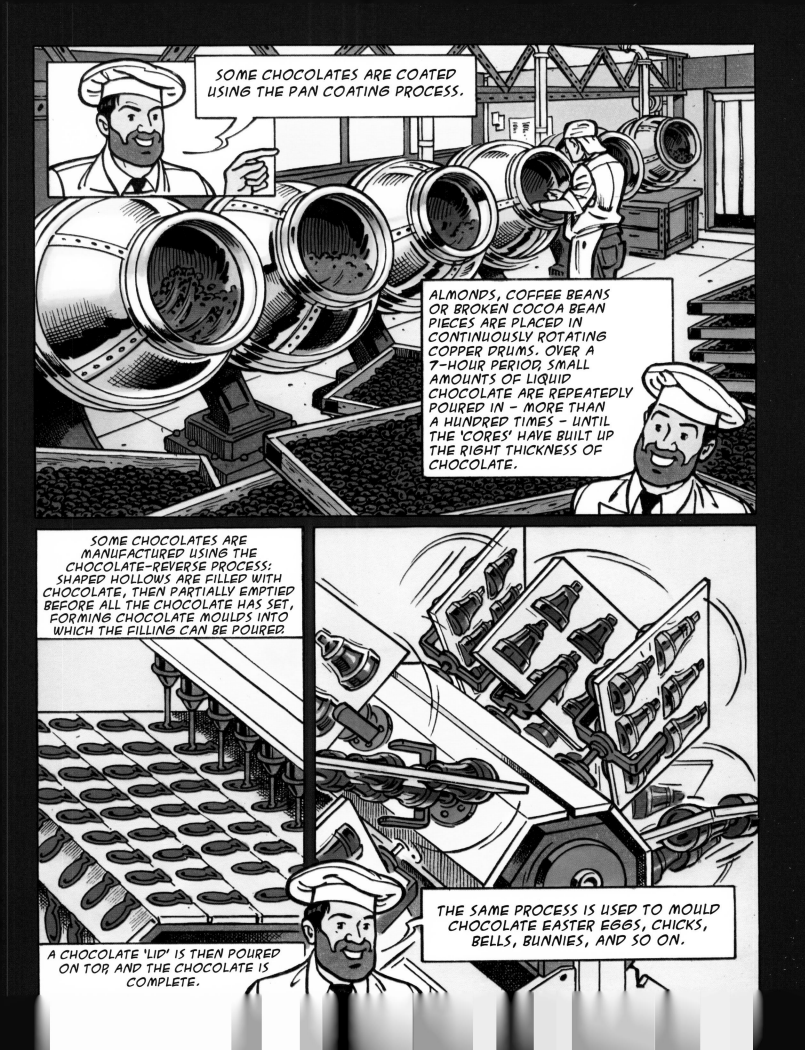

Chocolate is where the heart is

A family business

There is no doubt, making chocolate is an exciting venture! All the more so when producing the very best.... At each stage, from the selection of ingredients through to the perfect wrappers, excellence is the keyword at the Michel Cluizel chocolate factory. This excellence is based on a balance between past and future, between tradition and modernity, technical know-how and hand-crafting. The family's expertise, handed down over three generations, is an intricate weave of trade secrets and clever sleights of hand. It is strengthened by continuous innovation, in terms both of the products and of their development and marketing.

But who then are these craftsmen of chocolate, sensitive to the beauty of the object to be savoured as much as to its flavours? Here is how the story begins...

A family passion

In 1947 Marc and Marcelle Cluizel, pastrychefs of long standing, made their first chocolates in their kitchen. Michel, their son, had a passion for chocolate. From the day he was born he knew the aromas of toasted hazelnuts and almonds, caramelised sugar and chocolate which used to pervade his parents' workshop. At the age of 15 he became their apprentice, and then set up the company with them. The three of them formed a formidable team for thirty-five years. Since then, Michel Cluizel has been joined by his four children to pursue the family tradition. And naturally, as they too were born into the chocolate business, they share their father's passion; chocolate is in their blood.

Sustained by the strength of their financial independence and family culture, these owner-managers form the soul of the company. This is probably the last remaining small independent chocolate manufacturing business in France to work from cocoa bean to finished chocolates. Their total focus and their deep commitment to quality set the governing premise for the company, in which the tradition continues of using experienced employees to train new recruits.

Michel Cluizel and his children

The chocolate factory

The Cluizel family business is situated in Damville, in southern Normandy, not far from the largest town in the area, Évreux. Its ultra-modern buildings, set among fields of wheat and maize, overlook the small town where it originated. It enjoys an exceptional location, a hundred kilometres west of Paris.

The chocolate maker's tradition, a state of mind

Neither the company's size (200 employees) nor the presence of sophisticated computer equipment have altered its professional approach. Safety-film glass partitions create individual areas in which each worker is master of what he does for all to see. Under the attentive guidance of the Cluizel family, a creative management team monitors the successful functioning of this complex machine, whose major asset is its human factor.

Each chocolate maker is an experienced professional whose versatility enables him fulfil different functions according to the season. Easter and Christmas are undoubtedly the busiest times, requiring special organisation to meet increased demand. Chocolate is a fragile product whose intense lifespan is but short, and storage of the thousand items in stock at all times must be as brief as possible.

In the quality control department, the men and women of the company do more than just monitor product quality; they are constantly creating new chocolates, to ensure the Michel Cluizel product range develops and maintains vitality. Once a new product has been selected, perhaps a Halloween pumpkin, how will it be produced? This is the cue for the technical team to start work: chocolate makers, electricians, mechanical engineers, computer technicians, everyone works together to convert or adjust the existing machines: here the machinery is adapted to the product and not vice-versa.

In 1992 an HACCP (Hazard Analysis Critical Control Point) quality system was adopted by Marc Cluizel to guarantee complete food-safety. All staff wear lab coats and hats, and no watches or jewellery. No product ever travels back up the production line, ensuring there is no risk of contamination. Quality control at every stage of manufacturing guarantees impeccable food-safety and flavour.

"Quality at every stage is the company's motto".
Michel Cluizel

Research and creativity

Michel Cluizel's customer base, as varied as it is, shares a common requirement: the very highest quality.

Overseas customers discover it in Paris at the Chocolats Michel Cluizel shop. In one of the smartest districts, in the heart of the city (201 rue St. Honoré), they come to dream by the fountain from which pours a stream of chocolate and to admire the precious little treats rubbing shoulders with the most prestigious diamond necklaces.

Making a mould in the mould workshop at the Cluizel chocolate factory.

Innovation and creation

Knowledgeable enthusiasts, whether from France or elsewhere, love sophisticated tastes and enjoy discovering new ones. For them, Michel Cluizel has created the Pure Origins of the World and High Cocoa Content selection boxes, which provide the foundations for learning about chocolate. The chocolate discs they contain provide an enjoyable tasting exercise. Would you care for Noir de Cacao ('cocoa dark') at 72% cocoa or Noir Infini ('infinitely dark') at 99%? Everyone can surprise their taste buds and choose which flavours they prefer, whilst being guaranteed an ever-perfect equilibrium: the bitterness is perfectly controlled and no undesirable acidity is allowed to disrupt the fine aromas.

Michel Cluizel also works in partnership with the best professional pastrychefs and restaurateurs. The reputation of his range of 'semi-finished' workshop products speaks for itself. They include: "High Cocoa Content" and "Pure Origins of the World" couverture chocolate made with cane sugar and Bourbon vanilla pods; old-fashioned pralines and gianduja in rectangular tubs; cocoa nibs; traditional or innovative chocolate decorations, etc. Branded or non-branded ranges also take their place in pastry and cake shop windows.

Michel Cluizel and his two sons are creating new products all the time, to achieve even greater customer satisfaction. Like composers who know the value of each note of music, he and his children, who have chocolate "in the blood", have a sort of perfect pitch when it comes to the taste and aroma of each raw material. This enables them to create a new product mentally, before it is brought to fruition in the secrecy of their workshop.

A universal pleasure

The pleasure of chocolate has travelled the world. It is enjoyed in Europe, America, Asia and Australia. Whether as a bar or individual chocolates, as a drink or a cake, milk or dark, there is a form of chocolate to suit everyone, regardless of country, age and preference for bitter or sweet tastes.

The gift of a box of chocolates brings pleasure and awakens our five senses. As soon as the lid is lifted, the chocolate aroma fills our nostrils, then after the first general visual impression, we examine them individually and decide which one we will take in our fingers. If it is a nougatine, it cracks as we bite on it, if a crunchy praline, it crackles delectably against the palate, as does the sugar shell which imprisons a liqueur. Finally, there comes the moment when we can appreciate the mutually enhancing fullness of the enrobing chocolate and its praline, with its taste of caramelised almonds, or its ganache releasing the subtle flavour of vanilla or the stronger aroma of coffee. But the pleasure does not stop there as the box contains other chocolates, waiting to be chosen, to be transported to our lips, and to transport our senses once again ....

A good chocolate should be long in the mouth, like a good wine, and prolong the pleasure of its eating: its taste should linger on the palate. As soon as the taste begins to fade, comes the desire to try another, just to regain that perfect moment of bliss, a tiny fragment of eternity. Which is why Michel Cluizel recommends eating chocolate just a little at a time ... to enjoy the pleasure it brings for even longer.

A delicate union

But what best accompanies chocolate? What is the best drink to enjoy with it? Its complexity, based on a mixture of sweet and bitter, makes it hard to match. Chilled water, through its very discretion, is the most often recommended. However, certain naturally sweet cask-aged wines such as Port or Banyuls can give the very best of results. Not forgetting a cup of coffee whose aroma complements that of dark chocolate in the most magical of ways. And why not accompany chocolate... with chocolate? With "Minigrams of Chocolate" from Michel Cluizel, made with 72% cocoa, you can prepare a genuine cup of old-fashioned hot chocolate. Enjoy it with a few "Minigrams" straight from the packet!

THE PLEASURE OF CHOCOLATE HAS TRAVELLED AROUND THE WORLD. IT IS ENJOYED IN EUROPE, AUSTRALIA, ASIA AND AMERICA. A BOX OF CHOCOLATES PRESENTED AS A GIFT AWAKENS OUR FIVE SENSES...

AS SOON AS THE BOX IS OPENED, WE INHALE THE RICH CHOCOLATE AROMA....

TWO FINGERS PLUCK OUT THE ONE THAT APPEALS MOST.

OUR EYES DWELL LONGINGLY ON EVERY PRECIOUS JEWEL....

SIDNEY

.... WE SAVOUR THE MUTUALLY ENHANCING FULLNESS OF THE CHOCOLATE COATING AND THE PRALINE OF CARAMELISED ALMOND.

OR A GANACHE EXUDING THE SUBTLE FLAVOUR OF VANILLA OR THE MORE ROBUST AROMA OF COFFEE.

AND IF IT IS CRUNCHY PRALINE, IT CRACKLES DELECTABLY, AS DOES THE THIN CRUST OF SUGAR RELEASING LIQUEUR-FLAVOURED SYRUP. AND THE PLEASURE DOES NOT END THERE, FOR THE BOX CONTAINS MORE CHOCOLATES FOR US TO TASTE ....

Cocoas & their origins

The art of blending

Each type of cocoa deserves to be understood for its own intrinsic qualities. But each can also benefit from combination with other cocoas to make a fuller, more balanced chocolate. Herein lies the art of blending, which governs the creation of a chocolate. All too often, mass producers content themselves with a single African cocoa, or perhaps two, which produce a chocolate with no definite character. Michel Cluizel, however, blends at least nine cocoas selected from among the best in South America, Africa and Indonesia. This enables him to produce a chocolate that is long in the mouth and has a perfect harmony of aromas.

Cocoa origins

As is the case with wines, each cocoa has its own character. To initiate chocolate lovers into the finer points of these singular flavours, Michel Cluizel proposes a "chocolate sampler" selection box with seven kinds of Pure Origins chocolates from around the world. Each one, made with a cocoa from a single country, develops its own special personality.

The plantation series

In 1999 Michel Cluizel went even further and created a new generation of chocolates: single-plantation chocolates. These chocolates talk to your taste buds and acquaint you with the cocoa beans from one plantation only, the ultimate in terms of cocoa traceability. Since then Michel Cluizel has created four more dark chocolates and one milk chocolate in the "Premiers Crus de Plantation" single-plantation range. They are all to be enjoyed in the same way as you would embark on a wine-tasting party to drink and compare the big names in wines.

Concepcion plantation (Venezuela): Set in the Barlovento valleys, east of Caracas, this plantation has since 1902 been producing prime Caranero cocoa beans, fermented, dried and polished in the traditional manner. The chocolate made from these beans gradually reveals its racy sleekness in which intense aromatic flavours bloom at length, with hints of vanilla, spices, and caramel, ending with deep notes of mixed dried and black fruits.

Los Anconès plantation (Dominican Republic): On the island state of the Dominican Republic, in the heart of the Caribbean, the Rizek family has been producing exquisite cocoa beans since 1903, west of San Francisco de Macoris. These beans bring an elegance and freshness to this fine dark chocolate with a wonderful combination of aromas: liquorice at the front of the palate, followed by red fruits and a long finish of green olives, currants and apricots.

Mangaro plantation (Madagascar): Set in the Indian Ocean, in the rich valley of the Sambirano river, the Mangaro plantation lies on land where a forest of mango trees once stood. These cocoa beans produce "Mangaro", combining exotic fruit flavours with delicious aromas of spices and notes of acidulated citrus fruit.

Maralumi plantation (Papua New Guinea): On the island of Papua New Guinea, off the Australian coast, the Maralumi plantation produces sleek and racy cocoa beans. They give this mellow chocolate slightly roasted and spicy flavours, fresh notes of green bananas and acidulated flavours of red currants.

Tamarina plantation (São Tomé): It was on the island of São Tomé, on the Equator off the coast of Central Africa, that the first African cacao trees were planted in the 19th century. Near a beautiful beach fringed with tamarind trees, the cacao trees on the plantation give this chocolate the accents of its fertile, volcanic and marine soil. Roasted, herbaceous and liquorice notes mingle in a beautiful length on the palate.

COCOA CAN COME FROM ALL SORTS OF COUNTRIES THROUGHOUT THE WORLD. FOR OUR OWN CHOCOLATES, WE USE A VARIETY OF BEANS CHOSEN FROM AMONG THE VERY BEST.

GRENADA

TRINIDAD

MADAGASCAR

CONCEPCION PLANTATION
VENEZUELA

IN 1999 I DISCOVERED THIS SUPERB PLANTATION IN VENEZUELA, IN THE BARLOVENTO VALLEY, NOT FAR FROM CARACAS. ITS COCOA BEANS HAVE GROWN UNDER IDEAL CONDITIONS AND BENEFIT FROM MORE THAN A CENTURY OF TRADITION.

VENEZUELA

ECUADOR

COLOMBIA

BRAZIL

JAVA

PAPUA NEW GUINEA

GHANA

SÃO TOMÉ

SAN DOMINGO

53

Chocolate in literature

Whether gourmets themselves, or simply inspired to introduce their readers to the pleasures of fine food, many great writers have praised the virtues of chocolate.

In the 17ᵗʰ century, the Marquise de Sévigné, in her famous "Letters" to her daughter, praised the thousand good qualities of chocolate: *"I've decided to improve my well-being with chocolate; I had some the day before yesterday to digest my dinner, so I could enjoy my late supper, and I had some yesterday and I was able to fast until the evening. It had all the desired effects; that is what I like about it: it does what one wants it to do."*

Early connoisseurs

In his Almanach des Gourmands (1803-1812), Grimod de La Reynière, extolled the merits of Parisian chocolate makers. In 1826 Brillat-Savarin celebrated the delights which chocolate brings us in his Physiologie du Goût:

"During the war, cocoa was a rarity, and very expensive too: people tried to find a substitute, but all their efforts were in vain; one of the benefits of peace has been to rid us of these various brews, which politeness made us try and which were no more chocolate than a chicory infusion is mocha coffee."

And further on:

" 'Monsieur', Madame d'Arestrel, Mother Superior of the Convent of the Visitation at Belley, told me more than fifty years ago, 'when you want to enjoy a good cup of chocolate, make it the evening before in an earthenware coffee pot and leave it overnight. The night's rest concentrates it and gives it a smoothness which greatly improves it. God will not be offended at this small refinement, as He is excellence itself.' "

Michel Cluizel Collection

In the 20th century, literature and childhood

Anatole France, in his autobiography "Le Petit Pierre", published in 1919, nostalgically recalls childhood visits with his mother to the Debauve et Gallais chocolate shop, suppliers to the kings of France, in the Rue des Saints-Pères in Paris. The shop, which was restored in 1800, is undoubtedly the oldest chocolate confectioner's in the world and is still devoted exclusively to chocolate.

In 1964 Roald Dahl wrote a moving story about childhood and chocolate in Charlie and the Chocolate Factory, a novel which is often studied in French schools. What happens in Mr Wonka's mysterious factory, which no one ever visits and which produces the most delicious chocolate? That is what Charlie wants to know:

"Twice a day, on his way to and from school, little Charlie Bucket had to walk right past the gates of the factory. And every time he went by, he would begin to walk very, very slowly, and he would hold his nose high in the air and take long deep sniffs of the gorgeous chocolatey smell all around him."

And wasn't every French child brought up with a lullaby whose tune dates back to the 18th century?

Go to sleep, Colas my little brother,
Go to sleep and you'll have some milk.
Mummy's upstairs
Making a cake
Daddy's downstairs
Making chocolate...

Michel Cluizel Collection.

56

FAIS DODO COLAS
MON P'TIT FRÈRE,
FAIS DODO T'AURAS
DU LOLO.
MAMAN EST EN HAUT
QUI FAIT DU GÂTEAU
PAPA EST EN BAS
QUI FAIT DU CHOCOLAT.

Chocolate and health*

For close to 500 years, chocolate has been used throughout Europe for medicinal purposes. Some have credited chocolate with every possible curative property - sometimes absolutely genuinely - while others blame it for all sorts of disorders, often wrongly. What is the current situation? Let us attempt to tell fact from fiction!

Some old wives' tales

Contrary to what some people say, chocolate has no detrimental effect on: acne[1], bowel movements (there is absolutely no reason not to enjoy chocolate when constipated[2]), diabetes (why should diabetes sufferers not be able to enjoy chocolate[3]?), cholesterol (it contains only a very small amount[4] and all in all it contains more "good" than "bad" fatty acids[5]), or even the liver; the all too famous "crise de foie" ('liver attack') the French seem to suffer from is usually nothing more than indigestion (after over-indulgence), and has nothing to do with any reaction from the liver!

Some facts

Having said that, however, it must be remembered that chocolate contains elements (potassium, oxalic acid, copper, etc.) that some people would be best advised to avoid (if they suffer from acute renal insufficiency, urinary lithiasis, Wilson's disease, and so on).

Numbers 1 to 9: see bibliography, page 72.

What about cardiovascular disease prevention?

Much research indicates that eating chocolate could help prevent cardiovascular problems (heart attack, stroke). This highly beneficial effect is thought to be essentially due to the fact that chocolate contains substances known as antioxidising agents - flavonoids - which are able to:
- combat a complex chemical phenomenon (oxidisation of low-density lipoproteins) involved in the development of obstructive arterial lesions found in artherosclerosis[6],
- inhibit clumping of platelets ... and therefore blood clotting[7],
- lower blood pressure[8].

More recent surveys[9] furthermore suggest that such substances may also have a beneficial effect on certain forms of cancers or neurological complaints, and may retard the ageing process ... even increase age expectancy. These are only the preliminary findings of recent research, and remain to be confirmed. Watch this space!

To put it in a nutshell

Considering the amount of scientific research that has been carried out on chocolate, it can nowadays be said that for most of us there is absolutely no risk in consuming chocolate, and it can even be good for one's health ... if eaten as part of a normal, balanced diet and not over-indulged in, of course.

* Dr. Philippe Léonard (doctor of medicine), author of 'Le chocolat : un aliment santé ?', to be published.

FOR CLOSE TO 500 YEARS, CHOCOLATE HAS BEEN USED THROUGHOUT EUROPE FOR MEDICINAL PURPOSES. SOME PEOPLE HAVE CREDITED IT WITH A RANGE OF CURATIVE PROPERTIES – SOMETIMES VERY GENUINELY – WHILE OTHERS BLAME IT FOR ALL SORTS OF DISORDERS, OFTEN WRONGLY.

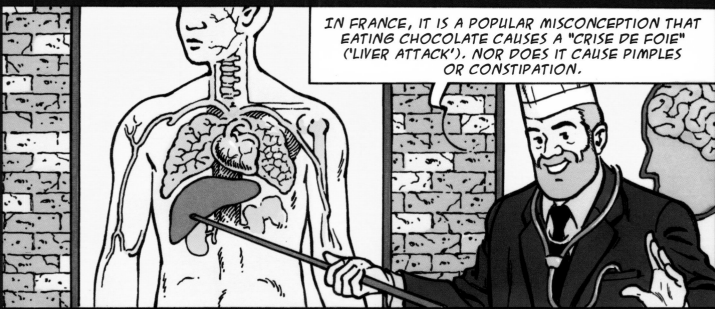

IN FRANCE, IT IS A POPULAR MISCONCEPTION THAT EATING CHOCOLATE CAUSES A "CRISE DE FOIE" ('LIVER ATTACK'). NOR DOES IT CAUSE PIMPLES OR CONSTIPATION.

COCOA CONTAINS A REAL COCKTAIL OF "PSYCHOACTIVE" SUBSTANCES (THEOBROMINE, CAFEINE, SEROTONINE, PHENYLETHYLAMINE, ETC.) WHICH IN LARGE PART EXPLAIN THE FREQUENT BENEFITS ...

THAT EATING CHOCOLATE CAN HAVE ON PHYSICAL AND INTELLECTUAL ACTIVITIES, ON STRESS, ON DEJECTION... OR, IN A WORD, ON "WELL-BEING"!

The chocolate seasons

Chocolate is enjoyed throughout the year. While there are two periods - Christmas and Easter - when it is particularly special, a gift of chocolate is always appreciated at any time.

When invited to dinner with friends, a box of chocolates is a treat for the whole family.

Christmas and family occasions would be incomplete if no one gave chocolates for all to enjoy after a meal.

At Easter, children run around the garden looking for chocolate eggs, chicks and rabbits hidden in the foliage. But who hid these treats? French Christian tradition has it that at Easter all the church bells, which have not rung since the evening of Maundy Thursday, go to Rome to make their confessions. When they return, they give eggs to good children who have kept their Lenten promises. In other countries, the bringer of treats takes on different appearances: in the Tyrol, it is a chicken; in Switzerland a cuckoo; and in English-speaking countries a rabbit, the Easter Bunny.

In Japan, the St Valentine's Day tradition is for women to give their male friends gifts. These days, they tend to be small boxes of chocolates.

Easter eggs

The Easter egg tradition is a very old one; in ancient times, it was adults who offered them up in sacrifice. In spring, in homage to Ceres, the goddess of fertility, the Romans sacrificed a hundred eggs on her altar. In the Middle Ages, this tradition associated with springtime renewal was adopted by the Christians: eggs decorated by students were blessed by a priest. King Louis XIV transformed them into veritable works of art, giving his courtiers porcelain eggs painted by Watteau, or others covered in gold.

Items in the Michel Cluizel Easter collection

At the end of the 19th century, tinsmiths made moulds for chocolate makers in the shape of hens, fish, or bells, so tradition could adapt to the tastes of younger food lovers. The chocolate egg was born.

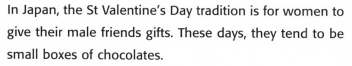

Storage

Chocolate, a food as delicate as it is delicious, has to be stored very carefully. It likes a stable temperature, around 18°C, with no sudden changes. Too hot? At above 25°C, its crystalline structure breaks down and a white film appears on the surface. Too cold? Putting it in the refrigerator or even worse, the freezer - as some chocolate makers do - turns it white and roughens its surface: condensation caused by excessive changes of temperature is fatal for it! Just as no wine expert would condemn a 1976 Pommard to the refrigerator, a chocolate lover should know how to preserve his favourite treat.

After storage, the moment of tasting arrives. Michel Cluizel's chocolate is designed to be at its best at between 20 and 22°C. At this temperature, its aromas will release their full richness onto the taste buds.

Note to chocolate lovers

We are all concerned by these simple precautions: the numbers of "chocophiles" throughout the world are increasing. According to a survey conducted in 1995, 60% of French people eat chocolate at least once a week, and 30% of them every day! Northern Europe traditionally has the highest consumption. Followed by Southern Europe, the United States and Japan.

The art of storage

The Michel Cluizel chocolate factory can quickly adapt its production capacity. This means its products are stored for a very short time before delivery, even in periods of heavy demand, such as Christmas. Even though storage time is short, Michel Cluizel has taken every precaution to ensure that his products are kept under the best possible conditions: following manufacturing and packaging, chocolates await shipping in a room in which temperature and humidity are rigorously controlled.

Shipping at the Michel Cluizel chocolate factory.

CHOCOLATES HAVE TO BE STORED VERY CAREFULLY: THEY REQUIRE A STABLE TEMPERATURE.

ABOVE **25°C**, THE CRYSTALLINE STRUCTURE OF CHOCOLATE BREAKS DOWN AND A WHITE FILM APPEARS ON THE SURFACE.

PUTTING IT IN THE REFRIGERATOR OR, EVEN WORSE, IN THE FREEZER TURNS IT WHITE AND ROUGHENS ITS SURFACE.

A CHOCOLATE LOVER SHOULD KNOW HOW TO KEEP HIS FAVOURITE TREAT.

OUR CHOCOLATES ARE DESIGNED TO BE AT THEIR BEST BETWEEN **20** AND **22°C**. AT THIS TEMPERATURE, THEIR FLAVOURS WILL RELEASE THEIR FULL RICHNESS ONTO THE TASTE BUDS. WE SHOULD ALL BE AWARE OF THESE SIMPLE PRECAUTIONS.

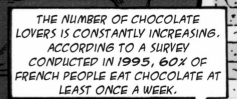

THE NUMBER OF CHOCOLATE LOVERS IS CONSTANTLY INCREASING. ACCORDING TO A SURVEY CONDUCTED IN 1995, 60% OF FRENCH PEOPLE EAT CHOCOLATE AT LEAST ONCE A WEEK.

OUR CHOCOLATE FACTORY ADAPTS OUTPUT TO DEMAND: PRODUCTS ARE STORED THE SHORTEST POSSIBLE TIME BEFORE DELIVERY, IN A ROOM WITH CONTROLLED CONSTANT TEMPERATURE AND HUMIDITY.

The Chocolatrium

Have you visited the Chocolatrium at Michel Cluizel's chocolate factory in Damville? It is THE place to get to know about chocolate. You will go through five distinct areas devoted to a different aspect of chocolate, covering more than 500 m².

The gallery

In the gallery you will discover the fabulous adventure of cocoa and chocolate. You will be able to read texts, look at photos, see objects and machines telling the extraordinary story that has travelled through the centuries and across the oceans.

The film

Comfortably seated, you will be shown a film telling you how cocoa becomes chocolate, and you will be given your first chocolate tasting lessons.

Discovering the workshop

There, right in front of you, you will actually see professional chocolate makers at work! Just the other side of a glass wall, they focus on their work, bending over their pots or over a small coating machine, reproducing the time-honoured traditional gestures of their trade. It is unfortunately not possible for visitors to see the actual manufacturing workshop as there are some company secrets to be kept, but also for food-safety and hygiene reasons. The Chocolatrium, however, gives you a true picture of Michel Cluizel's company: the chocolates being made in front of you are actually part of the day's output.

The diorama

Another door and you are taken back to the olden days, to a workshop of the days of yore. Stones, coppers, and crockery give you a glimpse of how things once were ....

The boutique

Your trip through the world of chocolate would not be complete if you did not have the opportunity to try a selection of our products. Let yourself go, and whether for family, friends, or for yourself, take the opportunity to indulge in a memorable moment of chocolate tasting. Who knows? The dreams of your children or grandchildren may yet be to become chocolate makers extraordinaire!

What visitors to the Chocolatrium have said

We enjoyed your presentation very much and your chocolates are wonderful!

La visite était très intéressante et captivante. De gourmands, on s'est délicieusement transformé en gourmets.

Mille merci pour ces saveurs chocolatées qui mettent du soleil en bouche.

Une visite très riche flattant tous les sens.
Un accueil très sympathique.
Un endroit à faire partager aisément pour les petits comme pour les grands!
Au plaisir d'une prochaine visite.

Vielen Dank für die leckere Schokolade!
Es war wunderbar.... hmmm....

Dorénavant, pour la messe, mes hosties seront en chocolat.
Chocorico!
Bravo

On ne mangera plus le chocolat de la même façon.
Fantastic! The smell of chocolate is wonderful and hugely entertaining to see how real chocolate is made.

A very interesting visit and made very welcome.

from the cacao

Cacao tree

Pods

Shelling the pods
opening the pod

Cocoa seeds

Fermentation
developing the aromas

Cocoa "beans"

Drying

Commercial cocoa beans

Transport

Main photo : cacao tree and pods.
Inset : cacao flower.

ee ▶▶ to chocolate

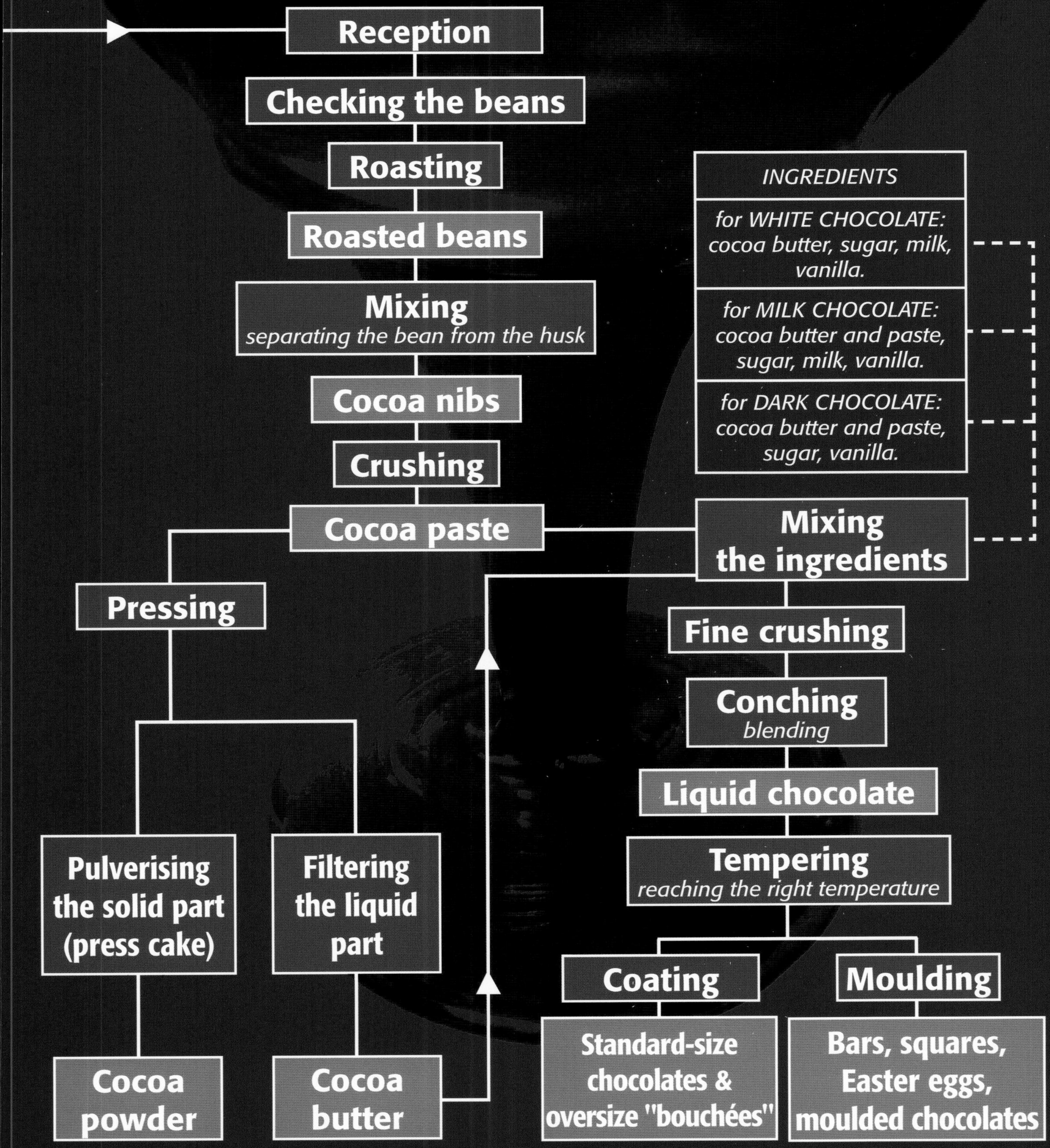

Reception

Checking the beans

Roasting

Roasted beans

Mixing
separating the bean from the husk

Cocoa nibs

Crushing

Cocoa paste

Pressing

**Pulverising
the solid part
(press cake)**

**Filtering
the liquid
part**

**Cocoa
powder**

**Cocoa
butter**

INGREDIENTS

for *WHITE CHOCOLATE:*
*cocoa butter, sugar, milk,
vanilla.*

for *MILK CHOCOLATE:*
*cocoa butter and paste,
sugar, milk, vanilla.*

for *DARK CHOCOLATE:*
*cocoa butter and paste,
sugar, vanilla.*

**Mixing
the ingredients**

Fine crushing

Conching
blending

Liquid chocolate

Tempering
reaching the right temperature

Coating

Moulding

**Standard-size
chocolates &
oversize "bouchées"**

**Bars, squares,
Easter eggs,
moulded chocolates**

The all-chocolate recipes of Michel Cluizel's grandchildren

Chocolate mousse
Nicolas, 10

For 6 approximately

Ingredients:
225 g. of chocolate
6 eggs
120 g. of caster sugar
2 soup spoons of crème fraîche

To make:
Melt the chocolate in a double boiler (bain-marie).
When the chocolate has melted, stir in the egg yolks.
Mix well.
Then add the sugar and the crème fraîche.
Beat the egg whites until stiff and fold into the mix.
Leave in the fridge overnight.

Marlène's yoghurt
and chocolate cake
Marlène, 10

For 8 approximately

Ingredients:
1 yoghurt (125 g.)
1.5 yoghurt measures of sugar
2 yoghurt measures of flour
½ yoghurt measure of oil
2 eggs
1 packet of yeast (7-8 g.)
2 yoghurt measures of 72% dark chocolate

To make:
Stir everything together, pour into a non-stick cake tin, and bake for 40 mins at 200°C.

Chocolate mud cakes
Claire, 16

For 5 approximately

Ingredients:
90 g. of 72% dark chocolate
80 g. of butter
30 g. of sugar
30 g. of flour
3 eggs

To make:
Butter some cup-cake tins.
Mix the eggs, the sugar and the flour together.
Melt the butter and the hot chocolate in a double boiler (approximately 40°C).
Stir everything together.
Fill the tins with the mixture.
Bake (200°C) for 5 to 7 minutes.
Demould from the tins onto plates.

Presentation suggestion: pour some custard into the plate and sprinkle with cocoa.

Bananas and chocolate
Romain, 10

For 1

Ingredients:
1 soup spoon of crème fraîche
1 soup spoon of sugar
1 soup spoon of grated dark chocolate
1 banana, sliced

To make:
Put the crème fraîche in a cup, add the sliced banana, then the grated chocolate and, to finish, the sugar.
Place in the fridge to cool before serving.

Stir everything together before eating.

Contents

A tribute to Marc and Marcelle Cluizel, my parents — page 2

Editorial — page 3

Michel Cluizel's first chocolates — page 5

The legend of Quetzacoatl — page 6

Cocoa beans, the Aztec currency — page 8

The Spanish and the New World — page 10

From the Spanish Court to the whole of Europe — page 12

Chocolate arrives in France — page 14

From craft to industry — page 16

Cultivating the cacao tree — page 24

The cocoa bean — page 26

From purchasing to conching — page 28

Different sorts of chocolate — page 30

Chocolates — page 32

Finishing the chocolate — page 40

Chocolate is where the heart is — page 44

The chocolate factory — page 46

Research and creativity — page 48

A universal pleasure — page 50

Cocoas and their origins — page 52

Chocolate in literature — page 54

Chocolate and health — page 58

The chocolate seasons — page 60

Storage — page 62

The Chocolatrium — page 64

From the cacao tree to chocolate (flowchart) — page 66

Recipes — page 68

Acknowledgments:

We would like to thank the following for their help:

- Madame Paule Cuvelier

  Chocolat Debauve & Gallais, 30 rue des Saints-Pères – Paris 7

- The American Museum in Madrid – Spain

- Mr. Thomas Sollich – Sollich (special machines) – Germany

- Mr. E. Catelain – Caffarel – Paris

- Mr. Gilles Pellet for his precious assistance as an archivist

  on the trade

- Thames & Hudson – London – United Kingdom

- Alain Bougard, author of "CH comme Chocolat" – Switzerland

Responsible Publisher: Michel Cluizel

Design and production: Hubert Privé – Ad litteram +33 2 32 60 13 13

Artistic management: Christophe Blin

Graphics adaptation: Thomas Peyrou

Editor: Sylvie Baussier

Medical editor: Dr Philippe Léonard

Drawings: Grimage

Photos: Patrick Forget

Photo credits: Patrick Forget, Hubert Privé, Cluizel Collection,

American Museum in Madrid

Printed in France - FOI

First edition October 2005, English

MICHEL CLUIZEL
ÉDITIONS

Avenue de Conches
F. 27240 DAMVILLE

Bibliography: the Michel Cluizel Collection

Barbier-Duval:
L'Art du Confiseur Moderne, Librairie Audot - Paris, 1879.

Albert Bourgaux:
Quatre Siècles d'Histoire du Cacao et du Chocolat, Office International du Cacao et du Chocolat, 1935

E. Duval:
Traité General de Confiserie Moderne, A. Réty - grand imprimerie de Meulan, 1905.

Ch. Joseph Barreta:
Manuel du Chocolatier, Mathias Paris, 1841.

Henry Dorchy:
Le Moule à Chocolat, Les éditions de l'amateur - Belgium, 1987.

Henry and Laure Dorchy:
Le Moule à Chocolat, Edition Ephemera - Belgium, 1999.

Anthelme Brillat-Savarin:
Physiologie du Goût, Furne et Cie - Paris, 1864.

Roald Dahl:
Charlie and the Chocolate Factory, French edition, Gallimard - Paris 1964.

Maison Letang:
Album de la Maison Letang fils, Aux Armes de Bretagne - rue Quincampoix, 82, and rue St Martin, 159, Paris - probably before 1860.

C. Trevor Williams:
Chocolate and Confectionery, Leonard Hill - London, 1953.

Philippe Sylvestre Dufour:
Traitez nouveaux et curieux du Café, du Thé et du Chocolat - 1685

Dr Paul Zipperer:
La fabrication du Chocolat - M. Krayn, Berlin

J. Fritsch:
Fabrication du Chocolat - Librairie des Sciences Pratiques Paris 6, 1923.

Dr. Philippe Léonard (doctor of medicine):
Author of "*Le chocolat : un aliment santé ?*" (to be published)
Pages 58 and 59 – Le chocolat et la santé
References:
1 – International Journal of Dermatology, 1977, 16, 6
2 – Le Concours Médical, 2003, 39/40. M.A. Bigard.
3 – Association de Langue Française pour l'Etude du Diabète et des Maladies Métaboliques (www.alfediam.org)
4 – Nouvelle Société Française d'Athérosclérose (www.nsfa.asso.fr)
5 – American Journal of Clinical Nutrition, 1994, 60
6 – American Journal of Clinical Nutrition, 2001, 74, 5
7 – Clinical and Developmental Immunology, 2005, 12, 1
8 – American Journal of Clinical Nutrition, 2005, 81, 3
9 – British Medical Journal, 1998, 317, 7174

Issues of Le Journal des Confiseurs, Pâtissiers Chocolatiers from September 1890 to December 1896 - 76 issues.

Issues of Le Journal des Confiseurs, Glaciers, Chocolatiers from January 1897 to December 1898 - 12 issues.

M. Martougin:
Codetalloz - Chocolaterie Industrielle - 1952

Cardelli - Lionnet - Clementot - Malpeyre & Villon:
Nouveau Manuel du Confiseur et Chocolatier - 5 – Société Française de l'Édition Littéraire - Paris 6, 1930.

Sophie D. Coe and Michael D. Coe:
The True History of Chocolate - Thames and Hudson.

from the cacao

Cacao tree

Pods

Shelling the pods
opening the pod

Cocoa seeds

Fermentation
developing the aromas

Cocoa "beans"

Drying

Commercial cocoa beans

Transport